4B

Reach
HIGHER

Practice Book

NATIONAL
GEOGRAPHIC
L E A R N I N G

Australia · Brazil · Mexico · Singapore · United Kingdom · United States

National Geographic Learning,
a Cengage Company

Reach Higher Practice Book 4B

Publisher, Content-based English: Erik Gundersen

Associate Director, R&D: Barnaby Pelter

Senior Development Editors:
Jacqueline Eu
Ranjini Fonseka
Kelsey Zhang

Development Editor: Rayne Ngoi

Editorial Assistant: Teh Chong Jin

Director of Global Marketing: Ian Martin

Heads of Regional Marketing:
Charlotte Ellis (Europe, Middle East and Africa)
Kiel Hamm (Asia)
Irina Pereyra (Latin America)

Product Marketing Manager: David Spain

Senior Production Controller: Tan Jin Hock

Senior Media Researcher (Covers): Leila Hishmeh

Senior Designer: Lisa Trager

Director, Operations: Jason Seigel

Operations Support:
Rebecca Barbush
Drew Robertson
Caroline Stephenson
Nicholas Yeaton

Manufacturing Planner: Mary Beth Hennebury

Publishing Consultancy and Composition:
MPS North America LLC

For permission to use material from this text or product,
submit all requests online at **cengage.com/permissions**
Further permissions questions can be emailed to
permissionrequest@cengage.com

ISBN-13: 978-0-357-36696-7

National Geographic Learning
200 Pier Four Blvd
Boston, MA 02210
USA

Locate your local office at **international.cengage.com/region**

Visit National Geographic Learning online at **ELTNGL.com**
Visit our corporate website at **www.cengage.com**

Printed at CLDPC, USA, 02-23

Contents

Unit 5: Invaders!

Unit 6: Treasure Hunters

Unit 7: Moving Through Space

Unit 8: Saving a Piece of the World

Name _____ Date _____

Unit Concept Map

Invaders!

Make a concept map with the answers to the Big Question:
When do harmless things become harmful?

Harmless Things That Become Harmful

5.1

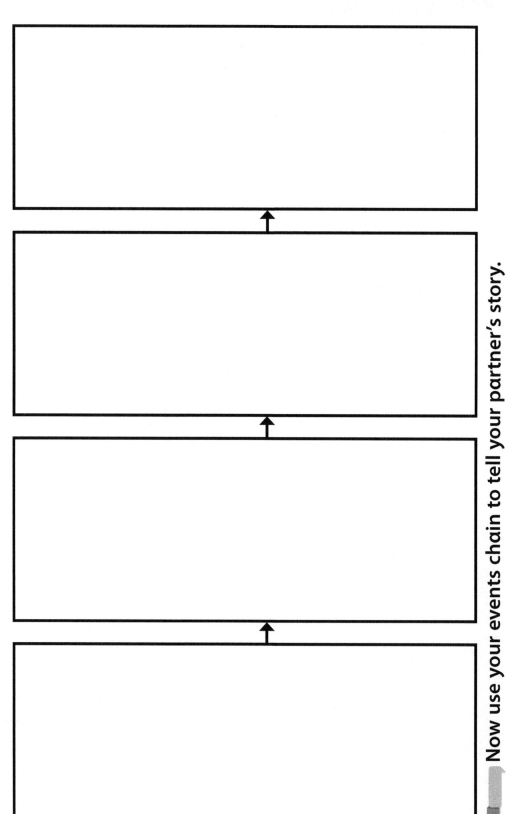

A Fast Growing Plant

Work with a partner. Complete the events chain to tell about your fast growing plant.

Now use your events chain to tell your partner's story.

© Cengage Learning, Inc.

Grammar

It's Nicer at the Park

Grammar Rules Adjectives

An **adjective** describes, or tells about, a noun.

Example: *a **tall** tree*   *a **hard** rock*

Add -**er** when comparing two items.

Example: **hard** → **hard_er_**

Add -**est** when comparing three or more items.

Example: **tall** → **tall_est_**

Write the correct adjective form.

I love going to the park. There is so much to see and do there.

There are ____*tall*____ trees by the swings. There are even _____
(tall)   (tall)

trees by the pond. Someone just planted a young tree. It is the

_____ tree in the park. I like to look at the _____ flowers.
(small)   (beautiful)

My favorites are the roses. They are the _____ flowers of all. My
(pink)

brother likes to play on the swings. He can swing _____ than I
(high)

can. Sometimes my dad will get on the swings. He swings the

_____ of us all.
(high)

▬▬▬ **Tell a partner about a park you have been to. As you talk, have your partner write down the adjectives he or she hears.**

Grammar

Creepy Crawlies

Grammar Rules Long Adjectives

To compare using **long adjectives**, use **more** or **most** instead of **–er** or **–est**.

Use **more** to compare two people or things. Use the word **than** in the sentence.	*Miki is **more** talkative **than** Shelsea.*
Use **most** to compare more than two people or things. Use the word **the** before the word **most**.	*She is also **the most** fearless girl in town.*

Make comparisons using **more** or **most**. Look for the words **than** or **the** to help you choose the right word. Write it on the line.

1. My friend Shelsea is ___more___ fearful than I am.

2. She calls bugs the _____ dangerous things on Earth.

3. "They are _____ distasteful than bees," I say.

4. "But they are not the _____ alarming things on the planet."

5. "Well," she says, "You're _____ fearless than I am."

6. "But you are the _____ awesome friend!" I answer.

▬▬▬ Talk with a partner. Use adjectives to compare yourself to a friend or to someone in your family.

Name _____   Date _____

"The Fungus That Ate My School"

Listen as your teacher reads. Follow with your finger.

1 When the students left for vacation, they told their teacher their fungus experiments were out of control. Mr. Harrison told the students not to worry.

When the students came back, fungus covered everything.

2 The fungus was in the hallway, the office, the library, the classroom, and the cafeteria. Mr. Harrison called in a fungus expert.

3 Professor Macademia arrived to get rid of the fungus. The Fungus Unit scrubbed everything and took the fungus away. Mr. Harrison promised not to hold more fungus experiments—until next year!

Grammar

Where It Stops, Nobody Knows

Grammar Rules Comparing with Adjectives

An **adjective** can tell **how many** or **how much**.	*The class had **many** problems.*
The words **more** and **less** are used to compare two items.	*The wall had **more** fungus than the floor did.*
The words **most** and **least** are used to compare three or more items.	*The light bulbs had the **least** mold of all.*

1. Take turns in a small group.

2. Spin the spinner. Follow the rule to use an adjective in a sentence.

Make a Spinner

1. Place one loop of a paper clip over the center of the circle.

2. Push a sharp pencil through the loop and the paper.

3. Spin the paper clip around the pencil.

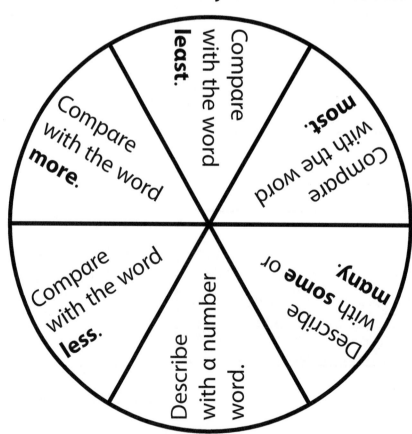

Compare with the word **least.**

Compare with the word **most.**

Compare with the word **more.**

Describe with **some** or **many.**

Compare with the word **less.**

Describe with a number word.

© Cengage Learning, Inc.

Reread and Retell

"The Fungus That Ate My School"

Use the events chain to write the order of events in "The Fungus That Ate My School."

The students study fungus.

↑

They leave for vacation.

↑

↑

Share your events chain and retell the story to a partner.

Name _____ Date _____

"The Fungus That Ate my School"

Use this passage to practice reading with proper expression.

"Fresh air, light, elbow grease, and a little help from my friends in the   14
Fungus Unit ought to get rid of IT," said Professor Macademia.   25

"Fungus Unit? What's a Fungus Unit?" Ellen asked.   33

"Special branch of the Sanitation Department," said someone dressed in   43
white, pulling a giant hose into the school. Other workers carried in shovels,   56
mops, and big lights.   60

"Action!" called one of them.   65

Suddenly the whole school was filled with whirring and clanking,   75
swooshing and scrubbing.   78

From "The Fungus That Ate My School," page 18

Expression

B ☐ Does not read with feeling.   A ☐ Reads with appropriate feeling for most content.

I ☐ Reads with some feeling, but does not match content.   AH ☐ Reads with appropriate feeling for all content.

Accuracy and Rate Formula

Use the formula to measure a reader's accuracy and rate while reading aloud.

_____ − _____ = _____
words attempted   number of errors   words correct per minute
in one minute   (wcpm)

Reading Options

"Mold Terrarium"

Use the fact cards to write down interesting facts you learn while reading.

Amazing Facts

An amazing fact about _____

is _____

I found it in the selection _____

_____   _____
           Name   Date

Amazing Facts

An amazing fact about _____

is _____

I found it in the selection _____

_____   _____
           Name   Date

Amazing Facts

An amazing fact about _____

is _____

I found it in the selection _____

_____   _____
           Name   Date

Work with a partner and share your facts. Take turns reading your facts aloud.

Name _____   Date _____

Compare Author's Purpose

Put a check mark by each purpose in the comparison chart that fits the science fiction story or the science experiment.

Purpose of genre	Science fiction: "The Fungus That Ate My School"	Science experiment: "Mold Terrarium"
Tells about a science idea	✓	
Tests a science idea		✓
Tells how to do something		
Is mostly fun to read		
Describes events that can't really happen		

Work with a partner to identify each author's purpose. Write sentences to explain why an author writes a science fiction story and why an author writes a science experiment.

Grammar

Gross or Good?

Grammar Rules Adjectives

Use **adjectives** to tell about color, size, or shape: **pink**, **brown**, **small**, **square**
Use **adjectives** to tell how something sounds, feels, looks, tastes, or smells: **loud**, **wet**, **slimy**, **salty**, **smoky**
Use **adjectives** to tell how something is used: **fishing pole**, **frying pan**, **sleeping bag**
Use **adjectives** to compare two things: **damper**, **more beautiful**
Use **adjectives** to compare more than two things: **biggest**, **most wonderful**

Choose an adjective from the box above to complete each sentence. Write the adjective on the line.

At night, Dad and I squeeze into our ____*small*____ tent. We hear

the _____ rain outside. In the morning, the sun is _____

than the day before. But the ground is _____ than before.

Gross! It has been invaded by _____ worms! Dad takes out his

_____ pole. "These worms are the _____ gift," says Dad.

Now we can catch the _____ fish of all!

▭▭▭ **Talk with a partner about a gross plant or animal you've seen. Use adjectives to describe and make comparisons.**

Thinking Map

Identify Problem and Solution

Work with a partner to complete the problem-and-solution chart about a problem in your environment.

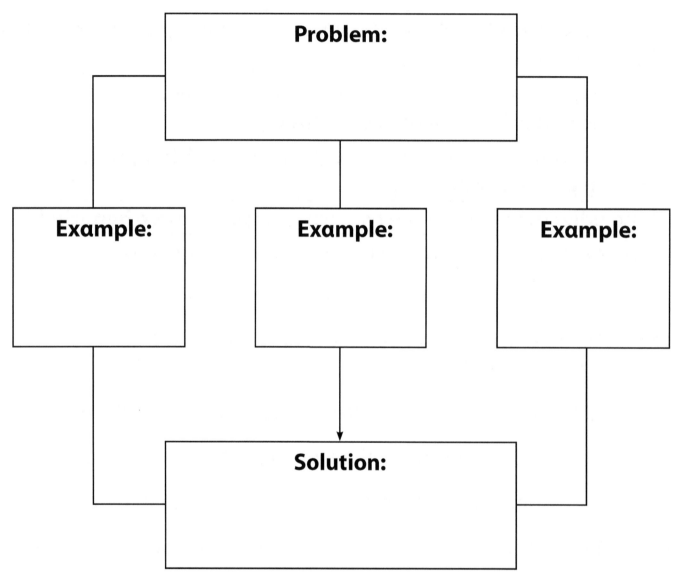

Problem:

Example:

Example:

Example:

Solution:

Share your chart with another pair of partners and see if you can come up with more solutions.

Grammar

Memory Match Game

Grammar Rules Possessive Adjectives

Singular possessive adjectives show ownership by one person or thing: **my**, **your**, **her**, **his**, **its**	**Plural possessive adjectives** show ownership by more than one person or thing: **our**, **your**, **their**

1. Make a card for each possessive adjective below. Make two cards for the possessive adjective **your**, as shown.

2. Combine cards with a partner. Place all the cards facedown.

3. Take turns turning over two cards and naming the words. If the two words match, use the possessive adjective in a sentence and keep the cards.

4. Play until all cards have been used. The player with the most cards wins.

my	your	her	his
its	our	their	your

© Cengage Learning, Inc.

Key Points Reading

"Aliens from Earth"

Listen as your teacher reads. Follow with your finger.

1

Aliens are plants or animals that invade ecosystems. They upset an ecosystem's balance. Animals and plants have always moved around, but in the past ecosystems changed slowly.

2

Humans sped up these changes. They traveled further and faster, and they took animals and seeds. Today, it is harder to maintain the balance of Earth's ecosystems.

3

Our ecosystems are no longer isolated from each other. The spread of alien species is a problem, but people can help by not carrying these species when they travel from one place to another.

Name _____ Date _____

Grammar

Just Outside the Window

Grammar Rules Possessive Nouns		

You can show ownership with **possessive nouns**.

One Owner	Add **'s**	*the dog**'s** tail*
More Than One Owner	Add **'** if the word ends in **-s**	*the students**'** desks*
	Add **'s** if the word does not end in **-s**	*the women**'s** names*

Write the possessive form of the noun on the line.

Last spring, a class found a ___robin's___ nest. Actually, they found
_____(robin)

two! The _____ nests were in a _____ branches. The _____
_____(birds)_____(tree)_____(children)

faces were full of smiles. Ms. Ramos began a study unit on birds.

The _____ shelves were full of books on birds. Many _____
____(library)_____(books)

pages explained how baby birds grew inside eggs. The children

made drawings. They put them on the _____ website. Now
_____(school)

other _____ faces are full of smiles.
_____(people)

 **Work with a partner. Find things in the classroom and tell who
owns them. Write a list: *Gabriel's desk, the students' coats.***

© Cengage Learning, Inc.

5.15

Unit 5 | Invaders!

"Aliens from Earth"

Complete a problem-and-solution chart to describe the main problem in "Aliens from Earth."

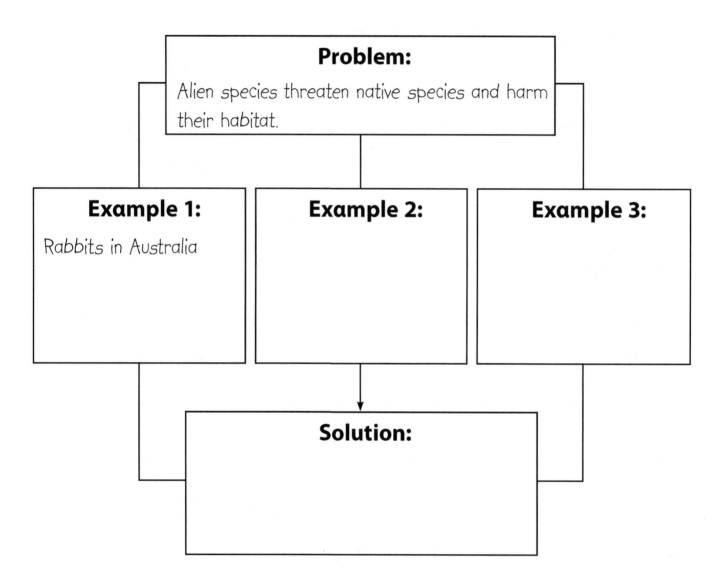

Problem:
Alien species threaten native species and harm their habitat.

Example 1:
Rabbits in Australia

Example 2:

Example 3:

Solution:

Use your problem-and-solution chart to summarize the text for a partner.

Name _____   Date _____

"Aliens from Earth"

Use this passage to practice reading with proper phrasing.

Many aliens arrive in the ballast tanks of cargo ships.	10
Filled with seawater, these large tanks help ships stay	19
balanced. The tanks are like aquariums in the middle	28
of the ship. When a ship arrives in port, it empties	39
its ballast tank. This action releases thousands of	47
worms, clams, snails, and other sea creatures into an	56
ecosystem where they do not belong.	62

From "Aliens from Earth," page 50

Phrasing

B ☐ Rarely pauses while reading the text.   A ☐ Frequently pauses at appropriate points in the text.

I ☐ Occasionally pauses while reading the text.   AH ☐ Consistently pauses at all appropriate points in the text.

Accuracy and Rate Formula

Use the formula to measure a reader's accuracy and rate while reading aloud.

_____ − _____ = _____

words attempted   number of errors   words correct per minute
in one minute   (wcpm)

"Island Observations"

Complete the first two columns of the K-W-L-Q chart before reading the journal. Fill in the third column as you read. Then write the questions you still have in the fourth column after reading.

K What I know	W What I want to know	L What I learned	Q Questions I still have

Tell a partner which detail was most interesting to you and why.

Respond and Extend

Compare Genres

Complete the Venn diagram to compare and contrast a science text with a science journal.

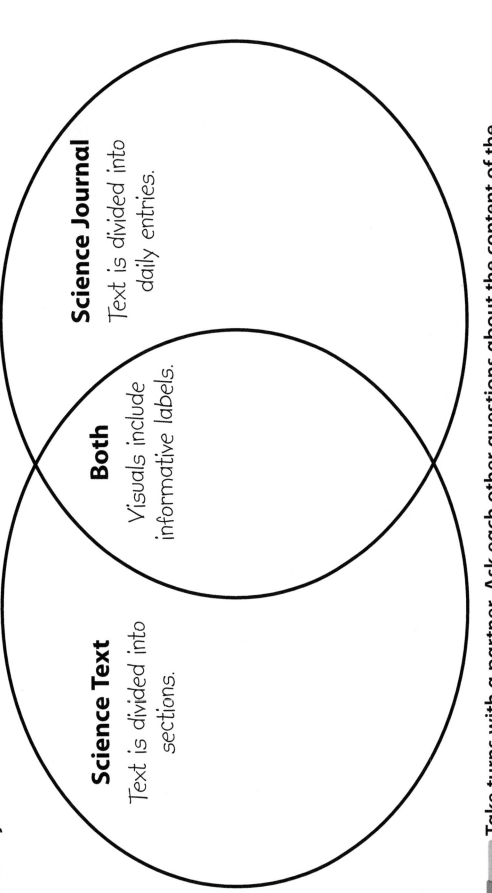

Science Journal
Text is divided into daily entries.

Both
Visuals include informative labels.

Science Text
Text is divided into sections.

Take turns with a partner. Ask each other questions about the content of the two selections.

Name ______________________ Date ______________

Grammar

Protect Your Habitat

Grammar Rules Possessive Nouns and Adjectives

Use **possessive nouns** to show that someone owns something.

One Owner	Add **'s**	*a rabbit's hole*
More Than One Owner	Add ' if the noun ends in **-s** Add **'s** if the noun does not end in **-s**.	*some animals' habitats* *the women's hats*

Use a **possessive adjective** to tell who owns something.

my *puppy* ***your*** *mother* ***her*** *cat* ***his*** *hat*

its *wings* ***our*** *house* ***their*** *skates*

Choose the correct form of the possessive nouns and adjectives.

A man's (man's, mans') exotic pet escaped! He was lucky to find ______ (its, his) pet in the park. Now the man watches the ______ (pet's, pets') behavior closely.

______ (Me, My) friends dumped ______ (her, their) terrarium plants in the yard. The ______ (children's, childrens') mistake could have been harmful. We must work together to solve ______ (us, our) problems.

Share ideas with a partner about things you can do to help stop the spread of alien species. Use possessive nouns and adjectives.

Writing Project

Ideas

Writing is well-developed when the message is clear and interesting to the reader. It is supported by details that show the writer knows the topic well.

	Is the message clear and interesting?	Do the details show the writer knows the topic?
4 **Wow!**	❑ All of the writing is clear and focused. ❑ The writing is very interesting.	❑ All the details tell about the topic. The writer knows the topic well.
3 **Ahh.**	❑ Most of the writing is clear and focused. ❑ Most of the writing is interesting.	❑ Most of the details are about the topic. The writer knows the topic fairly well.
2 **Hmm.**	❑ Some of the writing is not clear. The writing lacks some focus. ❑ Some of the writing is confusing.	❑ Some details are about the topic. The writer doesn't know the topic well.
1 **Huh?**	❑ The writing is not clear or focused. ❑ The writing is confusing.	❑ Many details are not about the topic. The writer does not know the topic.

Name _____   Date _____

Problem-and-Solution Chart

Complete the problem-and-solution chart and use it to write a persuasive essay.

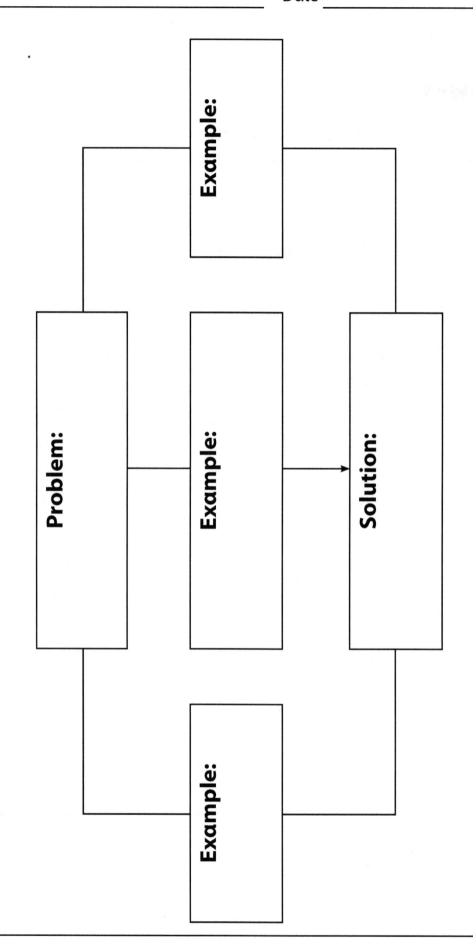

Problem:

Example:

Example:

Example:

Solution:

Writing Project

Revise

Use revision marks to make changes to these paragraphs. Look for:

- reasons that support opinions
- persuasive language
- worthwhile ideas
- details and examples

Revision Marks	
∧	Add
℘	Take out
⬭⟋	Move to here

Trash Trouble at the Beach

Trash on the beach creates problems. Because of this, I think it is bad to throw your trash on the ground.

People make the beach dirty. They leave stuff in the sand and water. Animals can get sick. So can people who swim. Trash harms natural habitats. It pollutes the sand and water.

If you go to the beach, do something with your trash. Put it somewhere. Maybe you can consider organizing a beach clean-up day. Disposing of trash in a responsible way helps all of us.

Writing Project

Edit and Proofread

Use revision marks to edit and
proofread these paragraphs. Look for:

- spelling of comparative and
  superlative adjectives
- punctuation of items in a series
- spelling of adjectives

Revision Marks	
^	Add
℘	Take out

Water pollution is bad for people animals and plants. When
people don't dispose of theires liquid waste properly, it creates
problems for the environment. We need to teach our's community
the responsible way to get rid of trash and other waste.

Water pollution in ours local lake means we can't swim or fish
there. Chemicals in the water can kill plants and animals that live
in or near the lake. An even biggerer problem comes from litter.
Rain sweeps trash on the street into storm. This trash ends up in
our water sources.

People must dispose of theirs chemicals and household cleaners
in a responsible way. They should never pour oil paint or household
cleaners down the drain. People can take these materials to the
citys hazardous waste center. This is the best way to create a
cleaner environment.

Treasure Hunters

Make a concept map with the answers to the Big Question:
How do treasures shape our past and future?

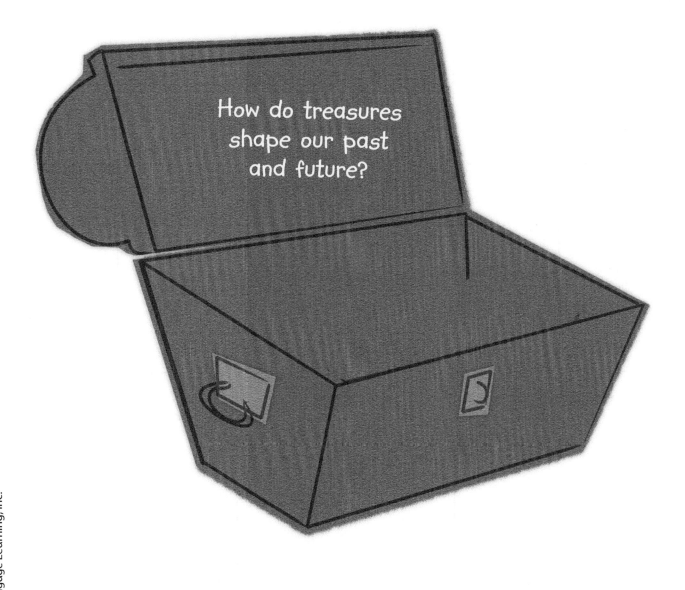

How do treasures
shape our past
and future?

Finding a Treasure

Complete a character map for one of your favorite characters. Tell how the character changes and why.

Events		Relationships

Character _____

Beginning	Middle	End

Use your character map to tell a partner how and why the character changed.

Name _____ Date _____

Today, We Are Pirates

Grammar Rules Subject and Object Pronouns

1. Use these **subject pronouns** as the subject of a sentence:
   I, **you**, **he**, **she**, **it**, **we**, **they**

2. Use these **object pronouns** after a verb or after a word like
   to, **for**, **from**, or **with**:
   me, **you**, **him**, **her**, **it**, **us**, **them**

Read the paragraph. Replace the word or words under the line with the correct pronoun. Then read the paragraph with a partner.

John and Ivan are pretending to be pirates. ___They___ plan an
                                              (John and Ivan)

adventure. John packs all his things. Then, _____ helps Ivan.
                                              (John)

John packs Ivan's bag for _____ . John opens the treasure map
                           (Ivan)

so he can study _____ . The pirates hope to find treasure so
                 (the map)

_____ can be rich. Ivan's mother wishes _____ good luck.
(the pirates)   (John and Ivan)

John and Ivan wave good-bye to _____ .
                                (Ivan's mother)

Talk in a small group. Express an intention. Use a subject or an
object pronoun in your sentence, or use both! For example: *This
spring, I plan to join our baseball team.*

Name _____   Date _____

"Treasure Island"

Listen as your teacher reads. Follow with your finger.

1

Jim and Dr. Livesey have a map to a treasure. They hire a ship and a crew to take them to Treasure Island. They will be rich!

2

Jim hears the crew talking. They are a pirate crew and are planning to steal the ship. They want to take the treasure. Jim and Dr. Livesey plan to fight them.

3

Jim sneaks into the pirates' rowboat. On Treasure Island, he hides in a cave. He meets Ben. Ben helps Jim find Dr. Livesey.

4

The pirates attack the fort, steal the map, and capture Jim. When they dig up the treasure, there are only two gold coins!

Jim, Ben, and Dr. Livesey go back to the ship. They leave the pirates on the island.

Grammar

Protecting Ourselves from Pirates

Grammar Rules Reflexive Pronouns

1. If you talk about a person or thing twice in a simple sentence, use a **reflexive pronoun** to refer back to the subject.

   Example: *Jim hid **himself** in the rowboat.*

2. Make sure your reflexive pronoun ends in **-self** or **-selves**.

1. Copy the eight sentence frames onto postcards.

2. Combine your cards with a partner's cards. Place the cards face down.

3. Take turns turning over a card and completing the sentence with a reflexive pronoun. Read the completed sentence aloud. If your partner agrees that your sentence is correct, keep the card.

4. The player with the most cards at the end, wins the game.

Don't cut _____ with that dagger!	A rat hid _____ in the ship's hold.	The pirates told _____ that they were not bad men.	Ben hid _____ on the island.
Can we steer this ship _____?	Maria taught _____ to read a treasure map.	You boys will make _____ sick if you sail in a storm.	I opened the treasure chest all by _____.

"Treasure Island"

Complete the character map to tell how Jim changes in the play.

Events	Relationships
joining the treasure hunt	Dr. Livesey Long John Silver

Jim
_____

Beginning	Middle	End
boyish but brave		

Use your character map to retell the story and show how Jim changed.

Fluency

"Treasure Island"

Use this passage to practice reading with proper expression.

JIM [*enters from offstage, alone and out of breath*]: I think	11
I've lost them. [*hopeless*] I was foolish. Why didn't I stay with	23
my friends? [*points upstage*] There's a cave! I'll hide there!	33
[*JIM goes into the cave.* BEN GUNN *enters the cave from offstage.*]	45
JIM and BEN [*surprised*]: Oh!	50
BEN: Are you real, boy? Who are you?	58
JIM: I'm Jim Hawkins. Who are *you*?	65
BEN: I'm Ben Gunn. For three years I've been alone here!	76
JIM: Were you shipwrecked?	80
BEN: No, I was marooned, left here to die. I stayed alive by trapping	94
wild goats. What I wouldn't give for a bit of toasted cheese!	106
[*grabs JIM's arm*] Tell me true, boy! Is that Flint's ship out there?	119

From "Treasure Island," page 93

Expression

B ☐ Does not read with feeling.   A ☐ Reads with appropriate feeling for most content.

I ☐ Reads with some feeling, but does not match content.   AH ☐ Reads with appropriate feeling for all content.

Accuracy and Rate Formula

Use the formula to measure a reader's accuracy and rate while reading aloud.

$$\underline{\hspace{3cm}} \quad - \quad \underline{\hspace{3cm}} \quad = \quad \underline{\hspace{3cm}}$$

words attempted   number of errors   words correct per minute
in one minute   (wcpm)

Reading Options

"Make a Treasure Map"

Predict what you think this selection will be about. Check the correct boxes in the strategy planner.

Step **1** What is the author's purpose for writing these

instructions?

❑ to tell a story   **OR**   ❑ to give information

❑ to entertain

Step **2** What is your purpose for reading?

❑ for enjoyment   **OR**   ❑ for information

Step **3** What type of selection are you going to read?

❑ **Fiction**   **OR**   ❑ **Nonfiction**

Do the following:
- Identify the characters and settings.
- Think about what happens and when it happens.

Do the following:
- Read more slowly.
- Identify steps in a process.
- Use maps and pictures.
- Concentrate as you read.

After reading, talk with a partner and confirm or revise your prediction.

© Cengage Learning, Inc.

Compare Texts

Complete the Venn diagram to compare the treasure maps in the reading selections.

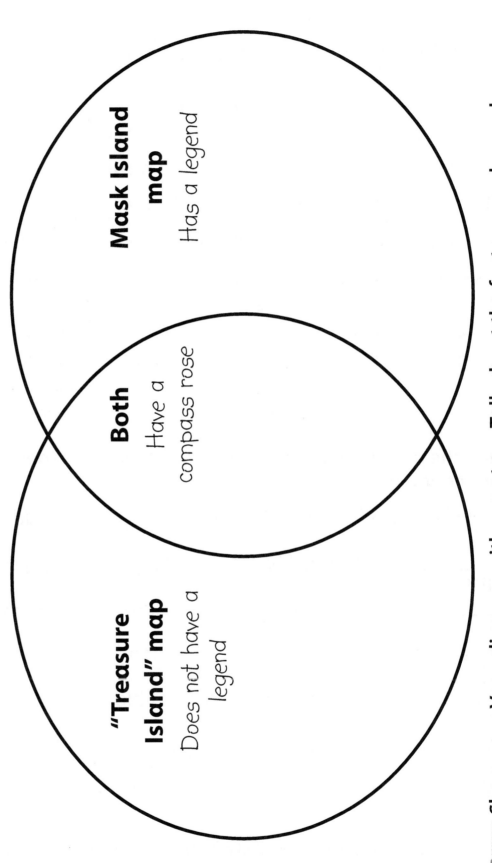

Mask Island map

Has a legend

Both

Have a compass rose

"Treasure Island" map

Does not have a legend

Share your Venn diagram with a partner. Talk about the features each map has.

Name _____ Date _____

A Tasty Treasure Hunt

Grammar Rules Pronoun Agreement

A **pronoun** can take the place of a **noun**.
The chart shows which pronoun to use.

Subject Pronouns		Object Pronouns		Reflexive Pronouns	
Singular	**Plural**	**Singular**	**Plural**	**Singular**	**Plural**
I	we	me	us	myself	ourselves
you	you	you	you	yourself	yourselves
she	they	her	them	herself	themselves
he		him		himself	
it		it		itself	

Read the paragraph. Replace the word or words under the line with the correct pronoun.

My little brother Jake likes pirates. ____He____ reads about
                                            Jake

_____ all the time. My mom and I are planning a surprise for
  pirates

_____ . _____ will hide a treasure. Then we will make a
   Jake   Mom and I

treasure map. Jake will use _____ to find the treasure. Mom
                                 map

helped _____ draw the map. But I hid the present by _____ .
           I   I

I hope Jake shares _____ with _____ . The treasure is a box
                      present   Mom and me

full of his favorite cookies. Mom and I made them _____ .
                                                      Mom and I

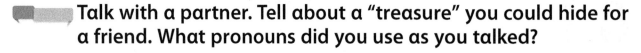 **Talk with a partner. Tell about a "treasure" you could hide for
a friend. What pronouns did you use as you talked?**

Thinking Map

Make a Timeline

Make a timeline to show the steps you took to find a lost object.

Timeline

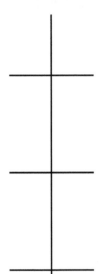

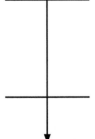 Use your timeline to tell a partner about your search for the lost object.

Grammar

Our Hidden Treasure

Grammar Rules Possessive Pronouns

A **possessive pronoun** takes the place of a person's name and what the person owns.

Singular	Plural
mine, yours, his, hers	ours, yours, theirs

Read the play. Complete the dialogue with the possessive pronoun that takes the place of the underlined words.

AISHA: We need <u>your treasure map</u>, Juan. Can you find
___yours___ ?

JUAN: No, and the pirates have _____ . They might follow
<u>their map</u> to our gold.

LING: But Captain Marcus lost _____ . <u>His treasure map</u>
sank with the ship.

AISHA: Oh wait! I found _____ . We can follow <u>my map</u>.
(*The three children follow Aisha's map.*)

LING: I think <u>our gold</u> is buried here. Dig! Soon the treasure will be
_____ again!

▬▬▬ **Work in groups of three. Choose roles and read the play aloud.**

© Cengage Learning, Inc.

Name _____   Date _____

"Diving for Treasure"

Listen as your teacher reads. Follow with your finger.

1

Alan Villiers wrote many books and took lots of pictures of his adventures at sea. One of his books, *Sons of Sindbad*, told the story of pearl divers aboard a ship called the *Bayan*.

2

Pearl divers were very poor and led hard lives. They had to dive very deep to find oyster beds, looking for oysters that might have pearls. They had nothing to help them breathe underwater. They made many dives every day.

3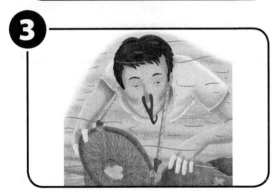

Divers were in debt to the ship's captain. Those who were lucky enough to find pearls kept only a small amount of the money. Many divers lost their lives, but some earned enough to escape poverty.

4

After the 1930s, the pearl industry in the Middle East declined. But it returned at the beginning of the 21st century. Pearl farming today is done safely.

Grammar

What Is This? What Is That?

Grammar Rules Demonstrative Pronouns

A **demonstrative pronoun** refers to a specific noun without naming it.

For one use: **this**, **that**	For more than one use: **these**, **those**
Examples:	Examples:
This is cargo.	***These*** are gold coins.
That is a map.	***Those*** are jewels.

1. Form groups of 4 to 6 players. Divide each group into two teams.

2. Together, teams choose 10 or more Language Builder Picture Cards. Half of the cards should show one object. The other half should show more than one object.

> Those are bars of silver.

> This is a sailing ship.

Play:

3. Team One draws and displays a card from the deck. Team Two uses **that** or **those** to describe it.

4. Team Two draws a card, displays it, and uses **this** or **these** to describe it.

5. Team Two draws a card. Team One uses **that** or **those** to describe it.

6. Team One draws a card and uses **this** or **these** to describe it.

7. Continue playing until all of the cards have been used. If you wish, shuffle the deck and play again!

© Cengage Learning, Inc.

Around the World

1. Write each Key Word on your passport.

2. Wait until you are a traveler or a challenger.

3. Listen to a definition of a Key Word and try to be the first to name the word.

4. Check off each word that you correctly name.

5. Check off all the words on your passport or make it "Around the World," and you win!

Passport

☐ _____   ☐ _____

☐ _____   ☐ _____

☐ _____   ☐ _____

☐ _____   ☐ _____

☐ _____   ☐ _____

Name _____   Date _____

"Diving for Treasure"

Complete the timeline to tell the sequence of events in "Diving for Treasure."

Timeline

Alan Villiers was born in Australia in 1903.

In 1923 Villiers made a voyage to the Antarctic.

Use your timeline to retell the article to a partner.

Name _____   Date _____

"Diving for Treasure"

Use this passage to practice reading with proper phrasing.

The divers held a heavy rock with a rope tied around it	12
to sink down to find the oyster beds.	20
They often went as deep as 18 meters,	28
which is roughly the height of a six-story building!	38
They hung a basket around their necks to collect the oysters	49
and bring them back to the boat.	56
Some divers could go as deep as 26 meters,	65
which was very dangerous. They had no equipment	73
to help them breathe. A diver just held his breath,	83
scraped the oysters off the rocks with a knife,	92
and put them in his basket.	98

From "Diving for Treasure," page 121

Phrasing

B ☐ Rarely pauses while reading the text.   A ☐ Frequently pauses at appropriate points in the text.

I ☐ Occasionally pauses while reading the text.   AH ☐ Consistently pauses at all appropriate points in the text.

Accuracy and Rate Formula

Use the formula to measure a reader's accuracy and rate while reading aloud.

$$\underline{\qquad\qquad} - \underline{\qquad\qquad} = \underline{\qquad\qquad}$$

words attempted in one minute	number of errors	words correct per minute (wcpm)

6.17

"La Belle Shipwreck"

Use the double-entry log to record what you read and your ideas about it.

Page	What I read	What it means to me

Tell a partner which detail was most interesting to you and why.

Respond and Extend

Compare Media Texts

Use the comparison chart to compare "La Belle Shipwreck" to a blog.

Feature	Web article	Blog
Title	"La Belle Shipwreck"	
Source of information	Texas Beyond History	
Date when written?	no	
Is the text in sections?		
Are there pictures?		
Does the information change often?		
Are there mostly facts or mostly opinions?		
Are there links to other articles and websites or definitions?		

 Take turns with a partner. Ask each other questions about the features of web articles and blogs.

Grammar

The Treasure Is Yours

Grammar Rules Possessive Pronouns

Use **possessive pronouns** to show that someone owns something.

Possessive Pronouns	mine	yours	his	hers	ours	theirs

A **possessive pronoun** does not come before a noun.

A **possessive pronoun** stands alone.

Answer each question with a possessive pronoun. Some questions may have more than one correct answer.

1. Are those their ships?   No, the ships are not ____theirs____.

2. Is this La Salle's ship?   Yes, this ship is _____.

3. Is this our shipwreck?   Yes, this shipwreck is _____.

4. Is this the woman's shoe?   Yes, this shoe is _____.

5. Are these your tools?   No, those tools are _____.

6. Is that your treasure?   Yes, this treasure is _____.

Ask a partner questions about classroom objects. Use language frames: *Whose _____ is this? Whose _____ are these?* **Have your partner use possessive pronouns to answer the questions. Then switch roles.**

© Cengage Learning, Inc.

Writing Project

Ideas

Writing is well-developed when the message is clear and interesting to the reader. It is supported by details that show the writer knows the topic well.

	Is the message clear and interesting?	Do the details show the writer knows the topic?
4 Wow!	❑ All of the writing is clear and focused. ❑ The writing is very interesting.	❑ All the details tell about the topic. The writer knows the topic well.
3 Ahh.	❑ Most of the writing is clear and focused. ❑ Most of the writing is interesting.	❑ Most of the details are about the topic. The writer knows the topic fairly well.
2 Hmm.	❑ Some of the writing is not clear. The writing lacks some focus. ❑ Some of the writing is confusing.	❑ Some details are about the topic. The writer doesn't know the topic well.
1 Huh?	❑ The writing is not clear or focused. ❑ The writing is confusing.	❑ Many details are not about the topic. The writer does not know the topic.

Writing Project

Character Map

Complete the character map for your historical fiction story.

Events		Relationships

Character: _____

Beginning	Middle	End

Writing Project

Revise

Use revision marks to make changes to these paragraphs. Look for:

- facts that are not accurate
- unrelated details

Revision Marks	
∧	Add
℘	Take out
⌒⌐	Move to here
⌒SP	Check spelling
⌐	Indent

Maria raced down the stairs. She remembered a show she had seen on television. A person on a ship had hidden in a little cabinet in the ship's galley. Maria had to grab the map and try. She could hear the pirates and sailors fighting on the deck.

Maria reached for the map and shoved it under her shawl. Then she dashed to the galley. A galley is a kitchen on a ship. Maria ran into the galley and squeezed into the tiny cabinet by the dishwasher.

Writing Project

Edit and Proofread

Use revision marks to edit and
proofread this paragraph.
Look for:

- pronoun agreement
- commas with introductory words
  and phrases
- correct use of: *their/there/they're,
  it's/its, you're/your*

Revision Marks	
⬭ SP	Check spelling
℘	Take out

   Right away Maria saw the pirates. She couldn't stop himself from

shaking. "Put down you're weapons!" yelled the pirate. " Its time to

give up!"

Unit Concept Map

Moving Through Space

Make a concept map with the answers to the Big Question:
What does it take to explore space?

Comparing Sports

Make a comparison chart to compare one of the sports on page 147 with another sport.

Sport	Where	Goal	Measure speed

Use your comparison chart to tell a partner about the two sports.

Grammar

In the Dark Sky

Grammar Rules Adverbs

Adverbs often describe a verb. Adverbs usually answer one of these questions: **How? When?** or **Where?**

How	When	Where
quietly slowly	soon yesterday	far there

Underline each adverb in the paragraph. Then categorize the adverbs.

<u>Yesterday</u>, Tana and I waited patiently for it to get dark outside. We had our telescope and our journals. Suddenly, it became dark. We eagerly looked through the telescope. I could see far into the sky. When I told Tana what I saw, she quickly took the telescope from me. The telescope made some items look as if they were nearby. Later, we wrote our observations in our journals.

How	When	Where
	Yesterday	
_____	_____	_____
_____	_____	_____
_____	_____	_____

With a partner, ask and answer questions about exciting things you have seen. Use three adverbs from the chart.

Name _____ Date _____

"What's Faster Than a Speeding Cheetah?"

Listen as your teacher reads. Follow with your finger.

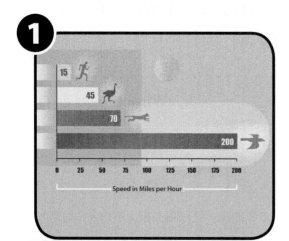

An ostrich is faster than a human, but a cheetah is the world's fastest runner. A peregrine falcon is faster than a car zooming along, but not as fast as an airplane.

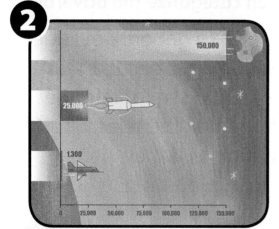

Propeller planes are fast, but a jet plane can travel even faster than the speed of sound. A rocket ship must go faster than a jet to make it into space. A space meteoroid goes six times faster than a rocket ship.

Yet, there is something even faster than a meteoroid. It is light. Light travels 299,338 kilometers (186,000 miles) per second. At that speed, you could circle the Earth more than seven times in one second. Most scientists believe nothing travels through space faster than light.

The Adverb Game

Grammar Rules Comparing with Adverbs

Some **adverbs** can be used to describe and compare actions.

- Add **-er** to compare two actions. Add **-est** to compare three or more actions.

- If an adverb ends in **-ly**, use **more** or **less** to compare two actions. Use **the most** or **the least** to compare three or more actions.

1. Take turns in a small group.

2. Spin the spinner. Add -er, -est, **more, less, most,** or **least** to the adverb in a sentence. Use the new adverb to tell more about a verb.

Make a Spinner

1. Place one loop of a paper clip over the center of the circle.
2. Push a sharp pencil through the loop and the paper.
3. Spin the paper clip around the pencil.

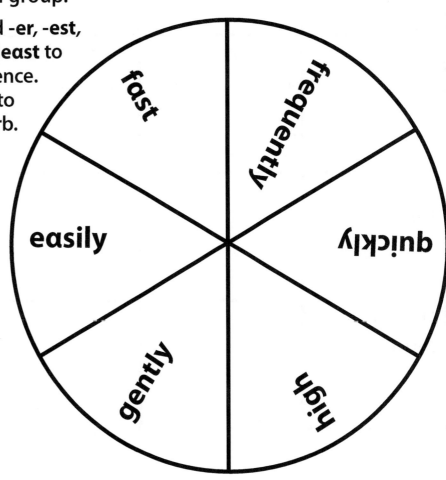

Name _____ Date _____

"What's Faster Than a Speeding Cheetah?"

Make a comparison chart for "What's Faster Than a Speeding Cheetah?"

Animal or object	How it moves	Fastest speed	Record
ostrich	runs on two legs	72 km (45 mi) per hour	fastest animal with two legs
cheetah	runs on four legs	113 km (70 mi) per hour	fastest land animal
peregrine falcon			
propeller plane			

Use your comparison chart to tell a partner how the animals and objects are alike and how they are different.

Fluency

"What's Faster Than a Speeding Cheetah?"

Use this passage to practice reading with proper intonation.

Hold on a minute. There's something much faster than even	10
the fastest meteoroid. It's something you see all the time.	20
Just push the switch on a flashlight. Instantly, a light beam	31
will flash out at the amazing speed of 299,338 kilometers	41
(186,000 miles) per second.	45
That's thousands of times faster than a meteoroid. At that speed,	56
a beam of light could circle Earth more than seven times in one second.	70
Most scientists believe that nothing can travel through space	79
faster than light. Who would have thought that the fastest traveling	90
thing in the whole universe could come out of something small	101
enough to hold in your hand?	107

From "What's Faster Than a Speeding Cheetah?," pages 160–161

Intonation

B ☐ Does not change pitch.   A ☐ Changes pitch to match some of the content.

I ☐ Changes pitch, but does not match content.   AH ☐ Changes pitch to match all of the content.

Accuracy and Rate Formula

Use the formula to measure a reader's accuracy and rate while reading aloud.

_____ − _____ = _____
words attempted   number of errors   words correct per minute
in one minute   (wcpm)

Name _____ Date _____

"Building for Space Travel"

Complete the dialogue journal with a partner as you read "Building for Space Travel."

What I think	What my partner thinks
Page _____ _____	_____ _____
Page _____ _____	_____ _____
Page _____ _____	_____ _____

Talk with a partner about the science report. Which of your thoughts are the same? Which are different?

Compare Fact and Opinion

Use the comparison chart to compare facts and opinions in the two selections.

	Facts	**Opinions**
"What's Faster Than a Speeding Cheetah?"		A peregrine falcon is magnificent.
"Building for Space Travel"	Constance Adams helped design TransHab.	

 Take turns with a partner. Use your comparison charts to ask each other questions about the facts and opinions found in the selections.

Grammar

Exercising in Zero Gravity

Grammar Rules Adverbs

Use **adverbs** to describe and compare actions.

Describe one action	soon	carefu**lly**	
Compare two actions	soon**er**	more carefu**lly** than	less carefu**lly** than
Compare more than two actions	soon**est**	the most carefu**lly**	the least carefu**lly**

Read each sentence and write the correct form of the adverb on the line.

1. Every day I enter the gym _____*sooner*_____ than my partner.
                                        (soon)

2. I walk in _____ than a gymnast.
              (eagerly)

3. I check that the equipment is attached _____ .
                                              (securely)

4. At first, I ran the _____ of all the astronauts.
                          (quickly)

5. If I keep practicing, I may one day run the _____ of all.
                                                  (fast)

6. I do pull ups _____ of all because I'm afraid of falling.
                    (carefully)

 Pantomime an action an astronaut might do in zero gravity.
 Have a partner use an adverb to describe or compare your
 action. Then switch roles.

Plot of a Story

Make a plot diagram about one of your favorite stories.

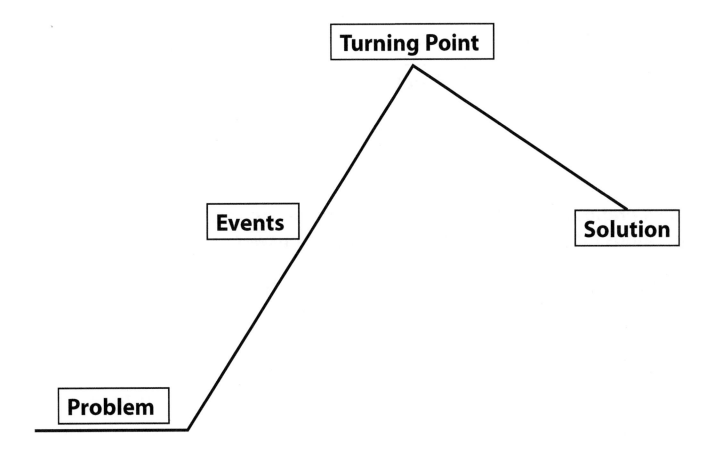

Use the plot diagram to retell your story to a partner.

Name _____   Date _____

Moon Walk

Grammar Rules Prepositions

Prepositions are small words. They show a relationship between other words in a sentence.

Use a **preposition** to show:

Location	Direction	Time
in, over, by, between	to, into, around, across, toward	before, during, after

Use a preposition from the chart to complete each sentence. Some questions may have more than one correct answer.

1. The astronauts train _____ *before* _____ their mission.

2. The rocket flies _____ the moon.

3. The rocket lands _____ the moon.

4. Two astronauts walk _____ the moon's surface.

5. They see stars _____ space.

6. The astronauts wear special suits _____ the moon walk.

 Tell a partner about a place you would like to explore or have explored. Use prepositions when talking about your exploration.

Name _____   Date _____

"The Moon Over Star"

Listen as your teacher reads. Follow with your finger.

1

In 1969, Mae was looking forward to astronauts landing on the moon. Gramps thought it was a waste of money. Mae and her cousins watched the *Eagle* land, but Gramps kept working on his tractor.

2

Gramps wondered why money was spent on a trip to the moon when there were so many people on Earth who needed help. Mae wondered what Gramps' dreams were. She realized that Gramps was tired from working hard all his life.

3

Neil Armstrong walked on the moon. People all over the world were listening when he said, "That's one small step for man, one giant leap for mankind." Gramps said it was something to remember. He told Mae to keep dreaming.

Is That So? Tell Me More!

1. Play with a partner.
2. Choose a picture from a magazine. Write your sentence as a caption.
3. Take turns building a related sentence with **prepositional phrases.** See how many you can use.

Examples: *I see a boy.*

*I see a boy **in a field**.*

*I see a boy in a field **with a rocket**.*

Paste your picture here.

Caption:

_____

_____

_____

Name _____   Date _____

Reread and Retell

"The Moon Over Star"

Make a plot diagram of "The Moon Over Star."

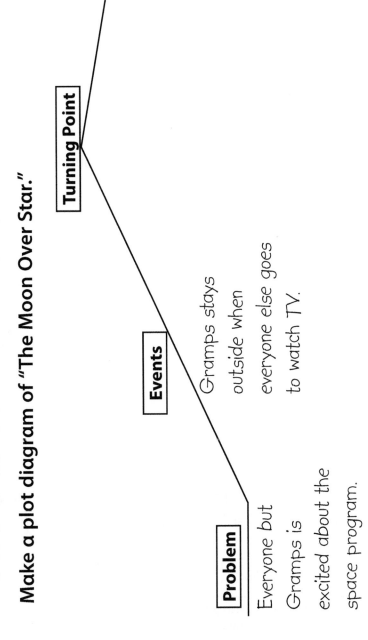

Problem

Everyone but Gramps is excited about the space program.

Events

Gramps stays outside when everyone else goes to watch TV.

Turning Point

Solution

Use your plot diagram to retell the story to a partner.

Fluency

"The Moon Over Star"

Use this passage to practice reading with proper expression.

Later, when it was as quiet as the world ever gets, Gramps	12
and I stood together under the moon.	19
"What's mankind?" I asked him.	24
"It's all of us," he finally said. "It's all of us who've ever lived,	38
all of us still to come."	44
I put my hand in his. "Just think, Gramps, if they could go	57
to the moon, maybe one day I could too!"	66
"Great days," he said, "an astronaut in the family. Who'd a thought?"	78
I smiled in the dark. My gramps was proud of me.	89

From "The Moon Over Star," page 193

Expression

B ☐ Does not read with feeling.　　　　A ☐ Reads with appropriate feeling for most content.

I ☐ Reads with some feeling, but does not match content.　　AH ☐ Reads with appropriate feeling for all content.

Accuracy and Rate Formula

Use the formula to measure a reader's accuracy and rate while reading aloud.

_____ − _____ = _____
words attempted　　　number of errors　　　words correct per minute
in one minute　　　　　　　　　　　　　　　　　　(wcpm)

Name _____ Date _____

"The First Person on the Moon"

Fill in the fact cards with information about Neil Armstrong or the moon landing.

Amazing Fact

An amazing fact about _____

is _____

I found it in the selection _____

_____   _____
          Name   Date

Amazing Fact

An amazing fact about _____

is _____

I found it in the selection _____

_____   _____
          Name   Date

Amazing Fact

An amazing fact about _____

is _____

I found it in the selection _____

_____   _____
          Name   Date

Work with a partner to share your facts. Take turns reading your facts aloud.

Name _____   Date _____

Compare Fiction and Biography

Use the comparison chart to compare fiction and biography.

Event or Fact	"The Moon Over Star"	"The First Person on the Moon"
Neil Armstrong was born in 1930.		✓
In 1961, President Kennedy said that America would send people to the moon.	✓	✓
Armstrong, Aldrin, and Collins flew to the moon in the summer of 1969.		
Armstrong was the commander of the mission.		
The first person to walk on the moon was Armstrong.		
The world watched on television.		
Armstrong said, "One small step for man, one giant leap for mankind."		
The astronauts placed a flag on the moon.		
The moon is 240,000 miles from Earth.		

Work with a partner to complete the chart. Discuss the facts that each selection gave about Armstrong with another pair.

Grammar

Going to the Moon

Grammar Rules Prepositional Phrases

A **prepositional phrase** starts with a preposition and ends with a noun or a pronoun. A prepositional phrase can:

	Prepositions
show where something is	in, on, at, over, under, above, below, next to, beside, in front of, behind
show time	after, until, before, during
show direction	into, throughout, up, down, through, across, to
add details	with, to, about , among, except, of, from

Add one or more prepositional phrases to each sentence.

1. I found a book about the moon _____.

2. The book was filled _____.

3. I was excited to take the book _____.

4. We have been studying _____.

5. My teacher liked the fact sheet _____.

6. My favorite photo is the picture _____.

⬛⬛⬛ **Use prepositional phrases to talk about space travel.**
For example: *I want to be an astronaut like Neil Armstrong.*

7.19

Voice

Every writer has a special way of saying things, or a voice. The voice should sound genuine, or real, and be unique to that writer.

	Does the writing sound genuine and unique?	**Does the tone fit the audience and purpose?**
4 Wow!	❑ The writing is genuine and unique. It shows who the writer is.	❑ The writer's tone, formal or informal, fits the audience and purpose.
3 Ahh.	❑ Most of the writing sounds genuine and unique.	❑ The writer's tone mostly fits the audience and purpose.
2 Hmm.	❑ Some of the writing sounds genuine and unique.	❑ Some of the writing fits the audience and purpose.
1 Huh?	❑ The writing does not sound genuine or unique.	❑ The writer's tone does not fit the audience or purpose.

Writing Project

Comparison Chart

Complete the comparison chart for your personal narrative.

Before	During	After

Writing Project

Revise

Use revision marks to make changes to these paragraphs. Look for:

- varied sentence types and lengths
- personal voice
- dialogue

Revision Marks	
∧	Add
℘	Take out

Fast Isn't Always Best

After school, my brother and I did our homework. I worked slowly. I took my time. I read the directions. I thought about what to write.

My brother worked quickly. My brother scribbled furiously. My mother told him to slow down. My mother told him to do his work carefully.

But my brother said loudly that he was done. He rushed outside. I was upset. I wanted to play outside too.

The next day, I proudly showed my mother my papers. The teacher had written a nice comment on my story.

My brother's teacher had asked him to do his homework again. I learned that being the fastest doesn't always mean you are the best.

Name _____   Date _____

Edit and Proofread

Use revision marks to edit and proofread these paragraphs.
Look for:

- spelling of adverb suffixes
- punctuation of dialogue
- adverbs and prepositional phrases

Revision Marks	
∧	Add
℘	Take out
⌒↗	Move to here

Swim season was almost over. You always win, said my friend
Ryan. You're like a dolphin.

I confident stepped off the platform. I waited patient for the
whistle. No one can beat me, I thought to myself. Suddenly, the
whistle blew and I dove into the pool.

I took an early lead. I won't have to work hard very to win, I
thought.

When I touched the edge of the pool, I was extreme shocked to
see the coach happyily giving Ryan a high-five.

What happened?, I asked.

Ryan beat you, said Coach Harris. He's been practicing and
training to get faster.

At that moment, I realized that being the fastest swimmer
requires a lot of hard work.

Name _____   Date _____

Unit Concept Map

Saving a Piece of the World

Make a concept map with the answers to the Big Question:
What's worth protecting?

Things that are worth protecting

Thinking Map

Mapping a Goal

Make a goal-and-outcome map about a project that you completed.

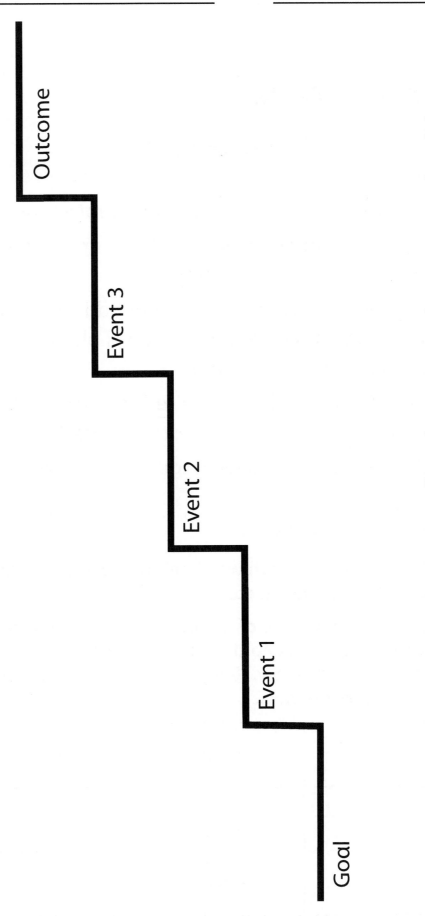

Goal   Event 1   Event 2   Event 3   Outcome

Use your goal-and-outcome map to talk with a partner about your goal and the steps you followed to reach it.

Grammar

Let's Agree

Grammar Rules Past Tense Verbs

- Add **-ed** to most verbs. Example: *protect* → *protect**ed***
- For verbs that end in **e**, drop the **e** and add **-ed**. Example: *value* → *valu**ed***
- Double the final consonant and add **-ed** to one-syllable verbs that end with a single vowel plus a consonant. Example: *plan* → *plan**ned***
- Change the **y** to **i** and add **-ed** to verbs that end in a consonant plus **y**. Example: *try* → *tr**ied***
- Change the spelling for irregular verbs. Example: *give* → ***gave***

1. **Play with a partner.**

2. **Make a card for each word below. Place the cards face down. Take turns turning over a card.**

3. **Spell the past tense of the verb and use it in a sentence. If your partner agrees, keep the card. If your partner disagrees, check the word in a dictionary. Keep the card if you were right. The player with the most cards wins.**

clap	hope	do	walk
go	spend	stop	reply
hurry	save	keep	enjoy

Name _____   Date _____

"Buffalo Music"

Listen as your teacher reads. Follow with your finger.

1

Molly lived in Palo Duro Canyon in Texas. As she did her chores, she listened to the sounds of the buffalo moving through the canyon. She called it buffalo music.

2

One day, Molly heard gunshots in the canyon. Hunters were killing the buffalo for their hides and hooves. Six seasons later, the hunters were gone. So was the buffalo music.

3

A neighbor brought two orphaned buffalo calves to Molly. Molly wanted to help them because she didn't want all the buffalo to disappear. Soon many people brought her orphans. Her herd grew to one hundred animals.

4

Molly heard that Yellowstone National Park wanted to rebuild its buffalo herd. She sent four buffalo to Yellowstone on a train.

The sounds of the canyon are different now, but Molly can still remember the faint sounds of the buffalo music.

Grammar

When Did It Happen?

Grammar Rules Present Perfect Tense

- Use the **past tense** if you know when an action happened.
- Use the **present perfect tense** if you don't know when a past action happened.
- Use the **present perfect tense** if a past action is still happening.
- To form the **present perfect**, use **has** or **have** and a main verb.

Read each sentence. Underline the correct form of the verb.

1. People (hunted/have hunted) animals throughout history.
2. During the late 1800s, people (hunted/have hunted) bison to near extinction.
3. One spring, Molly (received/has received) two orphaned calves.
4. She (worked/has worked) through the summer to save them.
5. Life in the canyon (changed/has changed) over time.
6. Recent settlers (made/have made) Palo Duro Canyon a different place.

Talk with a partner about different things you have done. Use the past tense and the present perfect tense in your sentences.

Name _____ Date _____

"Buffalo Music"

Make a goal-and-outcome map for "Buffalo Music."

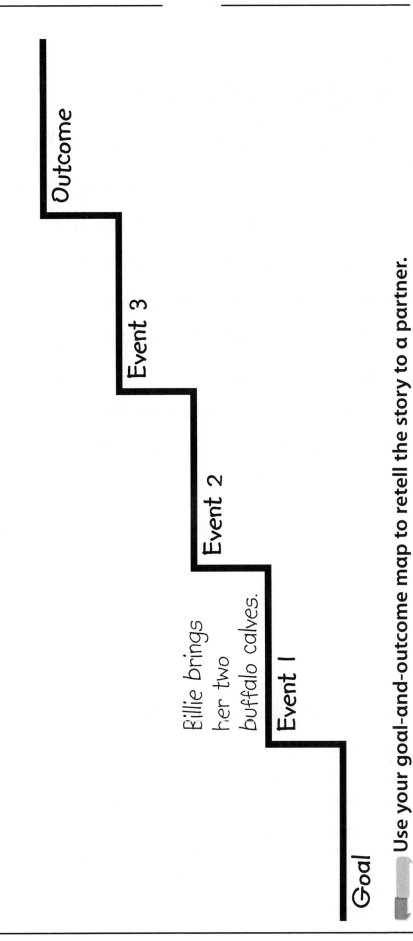

Outcome

Event 3

Event 2

Event 1

Billie brings her two buffalo calves.

Goal

Use your goal-and-outcome map to retell the story to a partner.

Name _____   Date _____

"Buffalo Music"

Use this passage to practice reading with proper intonation.

That summer, the heat fell as heavy as an angry fist.	11
The trails were deep with dust. The grass cracked like glass	22
underfoot. And everywhere, as far as the eye could see, the	33
bleached bones of the buffalo glistened white in the sun.	43
Within six seasons, the hunters were gone. So was the	53
buffalo music.	55
Oh, those were lonely, silent days! I was sure the only	66
song left in the canyon was the old whistle of the north wind.	79

From "Buffalo Music" page 222

Intonation

B ☐ Does not change pitch.   **A** ☐ Changes pitch to match some of the content.

I ☐ Changes pitch, but does not match content.   **AH** ☐ Changes pitch to match all of the content.

Accuracy and Rate Formula

Use the formula to measure a reader's accuracy and rate while reading aloud.

_____ − _____ = _____
words attempted   number of errors   words correct per minute
in one minute   (wcpm)

Name _____   Date _____

"Saving Bison From Extinction"

Fill in a K-W-L-Q chart as you read the selection.

K What I know	W What I want to know	L What I learned	Q Questions I still have

Talk with a partner about where you might find answers to the questions you still have.

Compare Fiction and Nonfiction

Use a Venn diagram to compare "Buffalo Music" and "Saving Bison from Extinction."

"Saving Bison from Extinction"

Both

"Buffalo Music"

shows how settlers lived in Texas long ago

Take turns with a partner. Ask each other questions about the content of the two selections.

8.9

Grammar

In the Past

Grammar Rules Past Tense

- Add **-ed** to form the **past tense** of most verbs.
- Drop the final **e** and add **-ed** to verbs like *live* (*liv**ed***).
- Double the final consonant and add **-ed** to verbs like *hop* (*hop**ped***).
- Change the **y** to **i** and add **-ed** to verbs like *cry* (*cr**ied***).
- Learn the special **past tense** forms of irregular verbs like *come* (***came***) and *have* (***had***).

Write the past tense form of the verb to complete each sentence.

Samuel Walking Coyote was a Native American who _____ to
(help)

protect the bison. One day, several orphaned calves _____ into his
(walk)

camp. Walking Coyote _____ the orphaned calves. Soon, his small
(raise)

herd _____ . He _____ his herd to people who _____ to let
(grow)   (sell)   (plan)

the bison roam free. William Hornaday _____ to protect the bison,
(try)

too. Hornaday _____ a small group of bison to the Bronx Zoo. He
(bring)

_____ the bison from becoming extinct by forming the American
(save)

Bison Society.

    **With a partner, write a paragraph to tell how bison were almost
    hunted to extinction. Use past tense verbs in your sentences.**

Analyze a Message

Make a fact-and-opinion chart about an ad, poster, or flyer you have seen.

Facts	Opinions

Use your chart to describe the ad, poster, or flyer to a partner.

Grammar

The Q and A Game

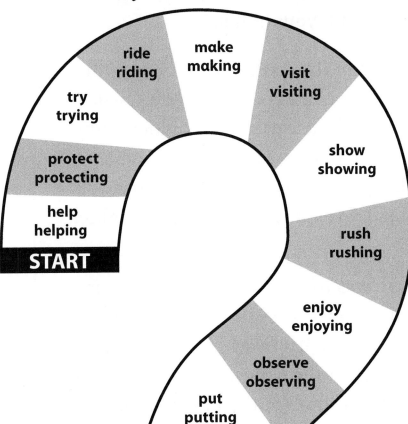

ride riding

make making

visit visiting

try trying

show showing

protect protecting

rush rushing

help helping

START

enjoy enjoying

observe observing

put putting

hide hiding

preserve preserving

study studying

fly flying

FINISH

Grammar Rules

1. Use the **past progressive** form of the verb to tell about an action that happened over a period of time in the past.

2. Use **was** with a singular subject.

3. Use **were** with a plural subject.

How to Play "The Q and A Game"

1. Choose a partner and some **Picture Cards**.

2. Use an eraser or other small object as a game piece. Flip a coin to move. Heads = one space Tails = two spaces

3. Use the past progressive to ask a question. Look in the selection and on **Picture Cards** for ideas. Have your partner use a past progressive to answer. Make sure your helping verb agrees with your subject.
   For example:
   Question: *What was protecting the treasures for many years?*
   Answer: *The tomb was protecting the treasures.*

4. Take turns. The first one to reach **FINISH** wins.

Name _____   Date _____

"Tutankhamun's Treasures"

Listen as your teacher reads. Follow with your finger.

When the sixth Earl of Carnarvon died, the butler at Highclere Castle showed the earl's son a hidden room. It contained treasures from ancient Egypt. It also contained the diary of Lady Evelyn, the fifth earl's daughter.

Lady Evelyn wrote about how excited she was to be invited to meet her father in October of 1919. He and archaeologist Howard Carter were working in the Valley of the Kings, searching for the ancient tomb of the Egyptian pharaoh, Tutankhamun.

After years of searching, they finally discovered the tomb. It contained many valuable treasures, including the mummy of the king. The Egyptian government kept half of the treasures. The rest were sent back to England.

Some people said the tomb was cursed, especially after Lord Carnarvon died soon after its discovery. Today, the artifacts found in the tomb are popular displays in museums and in Highclere Castle.

Grammar

What Will You Do?

Grammar Rules Future Tense

1. Use **will** plus a **main verb** to tell about a future action.

   Example: *I **will visit** a museum with my fourth-grade class.*

2. You can also use **am going to**, **is going to**, or **are going to**, plus a **main verb** to tell about a future action.

   Examples: *We **are going to look** at objects from the Civil War.*

   *Our teacher **is going to explain** the artifacts to us.*

   *I **am going to bring** my camera and take pictures.*

Choose a place you would like to visit to learn about the past. Write future tense sentences to tell about what you will see or do. Include both ways of telling about the future.

_____

_____

_____

_____

_____

_____

_____

Share your sentences with a partner. Check each other's sentences to make sure that the future tense is used correctly.

Vocabulary

Vocabulary Bingo

Play Bingo using the Key Words from this unit.

Name _____   Date _____

"Tutankhamun's Treasures"

Complete a fact-and-opinion chart about "Tutankhamun's Treasures."

Facts	Opinions
Ancient Egyptian artifacts were found at Highclere Castle.	England's such a dreary place.

 Use your fact-and-opinion chart to analyze the personal narrative for a partner.

Name _____   Date _____

"Tutankhamun's Treasures"

Use this passage to practice reading with proper phrasing.

I think this may have been the best day of my entire life!	13
We finally opened the door to the burial chamber. As I am the	26
smallest, I was the one to squeeze in first. Carter's assistant	37
tried, but he couldn't fit inside the small opening at all! He was	50
terribly disappointed.	52
This room has only one thing inside—a shrine. Carter says	63
that inside, we shall find the mummy of Tutankhamun. I suppose	74
some women would find this kind of thing terrifying, but I am	86
not one of those women.	91
Some are saying the tomb is cursed, but they are just silly,	103
superstitious people. Tutankhamun died more than 3,000 years ago.	112
We have nothing to fear from him. I just can't wait for the next few	127
days to see what the shrine contains.	134

From "Tutankhamun's Treasures," page 263

Phrasing

- [B] ☐ Rarely pauses while reading the text.
- [I] ☐ Occasionally pauses while reading the text.
- [A] ☐ Frequently pauses at appropriate points in the text.
- [AH] ☐ Consistently pauses at all appropriate points in the text.

Accuracy and Rate Formula

Use the formula to measure a reader's accuracy and rate while reading aloud.

$$\underbrace{\rule{3cm}{0.4pt}}_{\substack{\text{words attempted}\\\text{in one minute}}} - \underbrace{\rule{3cm}{0.4pt}}_{\text{number of errors}} = \underbrace{\rule{3cm}{0.4pt}}_{\substack{\text{words correct per minute}\\\text{(wcpm)}}}$$

"Saving the World's Oldest Library"

Complete a reflection journal as you read "Saving the World's Oldest Library."

Page	What I read	What it means to me

Compare journals with a partner. See if you asked any of the same questions. If so, discuss your answers. If not, take turns explaining why you asked each question.

Compare Text Features

Make a comparison chart to compare features of a literary text and an informational text.

	"Tutankhamun's Treasures"	"Saving the World's Oldest Library"
genre	historical fiction	
real or fiction?	real facts with some elements of fiction	
text features	photographs	
point of view		
author's purpose		
how you know the purpose		

Take turns with a partner. Ask each other questions about the features of literary and informational texts.

Grammar

A Library in Your Future

Grammar Future Tense

- Use the helping verb **will** along with a **main verb**.

  Example: *Our library **will move** to a bigger building.*

- Use **am going to**, **is going to**, or **are going to** with a **main verb**.

  Examples: *I **am going to like** the new building.*

  *It **is going to have** room for more books.*

  *Officials **are going to offer** more programs.*

Complete each sentence with the future tense. Use the main verb in parentheses.

1. The library ___will extend___ its hours.
   (extend)

2. It _____ early on Saturdays.
   (open)

3. Two teachers _____ there after school.
   (work)

4. They _____ students with their homework.
   (help)

5. The library _____ a movie section.
   (offer)

6. You _____ movies just like you do books!
   (borrow)

7. I _____ the new computers.
   (enjoy)

> **Use the future tense to talk with a partner about the library. What else will people be able to do there?**

Name _____   Date _____

Organization

Writing is organized when it is easy to follow. All the ideas make sense together and flow from one idea to the next in an order that fits the writer's audience and purpose.

	Is the writing organized? Does it fit the audience and purpose?	**Does the writing flow?**
4 Wow!	❏ The writing is very well-organized. ❏ It clearly fits both the writer's audience and purpose.	❏ The writing is smooth and logical. Each sentence flows into the next one.
3 Ahh.	❏ Most of the writing is organized. ❏ It mostly fits the writer's audience and purpose.	❏ Most of the writing is smooth. There are only a few sentences that do not flow logically.
2 Hmm.	❏ The writing is not well-organized. ❏ It fits the writer's audience or the writer's purpose, but not both.	❏ Some of the writing is smooth. Many sentences do not flow smoothly.
1 Huh?	❏ The writing is not organized at all. ❏ It does not fit the writer's audience or purpose.	❏ The sentences do not flow smoothly or logically.

Name _____   Date _____

T-Chart

Complete the T-Chart for your literary response.

What I liked	What I didn't like

Revise

Use revision marks to make changes to these paragraphs. Look for:

- a short summary of the literature
- a clearly stated opinion
- reasons that support the opinion
- details that help develop ideas

Revision Marks	
∧	Add
ℓ	Take out
⟲⟍	Move to here

"A Million Trees"
by Beatriz
Reviewed by Latifah Malouf

"A Million Trees" is a poem written by Beatriz, a student like us, to tell one thing she can do to save a piece of the earth. I liked this poem but I wish it was longer.

I am worried about pollution. The reason Beatriz gave for planting trees. She said, "The trees will be of service. The air will be much cleaner."

The poem was fun to read. I liked the rhyme and the images it made in my mind. The squirrels will adore it,

Writing Project

Edit and Proofread

**Use the revision marks to edit and proofread these paragraphs.
Look for:**

- **suffixes and base words**
- **regular and irregular
  past-tense verbs**
- **future tense**
- **punctuating titles**

Revision Marks	
∧	Add
℘	Take out
⌒⌒	Move to here
⌒ SP	Check spelling
≡	Capitalize

This is one of the best articles I've read about a neighborhood environmental program. It made me want to start a program in my own neighborhood. I am especially interested when the author wrote, "My life and the lives of all my neighbors changeed after we began working together." The article made me hopful.

I felt really sad when I readed the writer's comments about huge amounts of waste, so I will take her recommendation. I am go to read the article titled How to Start a recycling program in Your Own Neighborhood next week.

Last year, I carryed our neighborhood newspapers to the Recycling Center. The article made me feel proud of our efforts. I goed with my entire family to get this done.

Photographic Credits

5.1 Paulius Beinaravicius/Shutterstock.com. 8.13 (t) Matthew Lloyd/Getty Images. (tc) Historica Graphica Collection/AGE Fotostock. (bc) Gustavo Caballero/Getty Images. (b) John Keates/Alamy Stock Photo